GREAT CARTOONS
OF THE WORLD

GREAT CARTOONS

OF THE WORLD

BY THE WORLD'S FOREMOST CARTOONISTS

SIXTH SERIES

EDITED BY **JOHN BAILEY**

CROWN PUBLISHERS, INC., NEW YORK

Acknowledgments and thanks are gratefully
made to the following publishers and cartoonists
for permitting the use of the cartoons appearing in this book:

THE PUBLISHERS:

Czechoslovak Life, Dikobraz, Editions Denoël, Look, The New Yorker, Punch, The
Saturday Evening Post

THE CARTOONISTS:

Charles Addams, Miroslav Barták, Bosc, Whitney Darrow, Jr., Chon Day, Robert Day,
Eldon Dedini, Boris Drucker, Michael ffolkes, John Glashan, Alex Graham, Stanislav
Holý, Stan Hunt, Edward Koren, Anatol Kovarsky, Lee Lorenz, Charles E. Martin, Frank
Modell, Guillermo Mordillo, Hans Moser, Tony Munzlinger, William O'Brian, Terence
Parkes, George Price, Donald Reilly, Vladimir Rencin, Mischa Richter, Charles Saxon,
Jean-Jacques Sempé, Vahan Shirvanian, Claude Smith, Ton Smits, Leslie Starke, Jules
Stauber, William Steig, James Stevenson, Norman Thelwell, Barney Tobey.

© 1972, by Crown Publishers, Inc.
Library of Congress Catalog Card Number: 72-84295
ISBN: 0-517-500949
Printed in the U.S.A.
Published simultaneously in Canada by General Publishing Company Limited

Jacket design and layout by Laura Jean Allen

Most great cartoons are either timely or timeless. The timeless cartoon is beyond the fashion of the period .A Rembrandt portrait has so much truth in it that it survives the fact that the subject is an insignificant Dutchman. In a similar way, the timeless cartoon has little to do with clothing, and is apt to dress its characters in neuter fashion, in the way of Thurber and Lear—a primitive, amoebic form that transcends style and becomes art.

Oddly enough, the timeless cartoon has to do with the Eternal Truth. When you fall over sideways from laughing, it is because the cartoonist has produced his humor and simultaneously has touched upon such subjects as man's search for love, understanding, peace, joy, and power.

The timely cartoonist, however, does not deal with such issues. After an eight-o'clock orange juice, he crouches in his favorite chair with the morning newspaper and an enormous pair of shears, and notes happily that the new cars are falling apart, that the prices of food, clothing, and entertainment have gone up, that women are having terrible problems with their hair, with their hair sprays, and with their hair thicknesses. He observes that mod styles are already outdated, and is delighted to see that women are beginning to wear awful-looking six-inch clog heels. All grist for his mill.

The cartoonist makes the truth recognizable, the invisible visible. This is what Daumier did in his caricatures. And in Rembrandt's paintings, one even sees people one recognizes. This is not so with the work of more stylized painters, such as Vermeer, or Raphael, whose paintings are beautiful and to be admired, but not because their people are alive and breathing. Yet the light in Vermeer's paintings *is* somehow timeless, and easily recognizable as true. The essential truth of the gesture can be seen in the work of other artists, for example Rowlandson, whose work was timely, yet also timeless, because his whole effort was bent toward showing the expressions, attitudes, and gestures of greed, lust, and sloth.

Timelessness is usually the result of showing the truth of the human condition, and of the naked emotion. The essential emotions—love, hate, fear—never change. The cartoonist has difficulty demonstrating the sheer truth in such an irrepressible way as to make you laugh. To begin with, it is almost necessary for him to be a genius. The timely cartoon, on the other hand, is easier to create because the material is always at hand.

Some cartoons contain elements of both timeliness and timelessness. Modell's upside-down stocking, "You call that hung by the chimney with care?" shows a contemporary child within the context of timeless Christmas. It is the father who has the sense of the historic Christmas.

Thelwell's ". . . and this is the present duke . . ." depicts a moppet with titled blood in his veins, wearing a cowboy suit. The outrageous juxtaposition of the small boy with the great hall brings together the timelessness and the timely by reducing the glorious figure of the duke to the level of any kid in Hoboken.

Addams joins two civilizations with his medicine man whose patient is suffering from an iron deficiency. The professional has always had his limitations, and this cartoon is a lovely comment on human fallibility.

Reilly's "We've run out of virgins, O Mighty One!" really requires that the reader be a person of some culture, with a knowledge of prehistory, to fully appreciate the point. But no one would have difficulty in understanding that the cartoon is in fact a very timely comment on the ubiquitous tourist, who is always finding himself in an ancient scene, equipped with his shoebox-lunch attitude.

Steig's "Come to bed" is a great cartoon that transcends the frame of bossy wife and weak fish who needs to be bossed. It reaches into history, and, in so doing, reveals a bit of everyone's childhood.

Darrow's characters in "We're air-conditioned, but we're on the blink" equate themselves not only with air-conditioning, but with complete dependence on their possessions.

Saxon's "I grant your point, but not because I agree with you. I'm under sedation" is a timely comment on our contemporary use of drugs to get through life. It also demonstrates the artist's usual keen eye on fashion, and the timeless truth of gesture.

Koren's telephone operator, who may spend her vacation in Area Code 603, is pure timeliness, and depends for its humor on the fact that all our lives are slowly being reduced to computer-like digits.

Dedini's "I think our commune is very, very fortunate to have you and your know-how, David" is a masterpiece that perfectly catches the idiocy of those young people who have no background, no sense of history, but who think that everything is original with them.

It is rare for any artist to treat of timeless issues. Very little art of any kind has survived. The timely cartoonist, by contrast, must be ahead of his time and be able to predict a trend. When something new appears he must decide whether or not it is going to fizzle out before he can get his cartoon to market. He must think quickly and think ahead in order to avoid turning in dated work. He deals not only with what is generally current, but with what happened last week and with what will happen next week.

It is a common experience to try to remember a funny cartoon, and not quite be able to remember it. Too many fine cartoons are thrown out with the fish. This book, then, is an attempt to put some of the best cartoons between hard covers, where they will be safe. I am perfectly sure that some of them will be valid twenty years hence. And—timelessness is tricky—I am pretty sure that at least a few will be valid a hundred years from now.

JOHN BAILEY
New York City, 1972

"Were there any important messages for the men in the audience while I was out?"

"For heaven's sake, Watson, the Baskervilles are only away for the month."

Terence Parkes © Punch

Terence Parkes © Punch

Terence Parkes © Punch

"You call that hung by the chimney with care?"

MENS AIRSTYLING

MENS HAIRSTYLING

"Here comes Charlie. Let's have a rubber of bridge."

MENS
AIRSTYLING

C·E·M.

"Have you been taking the powdered newts regularly?"

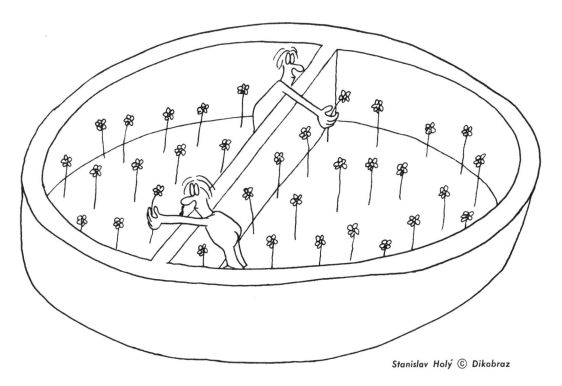

Stanislav Holý © Dikobraz

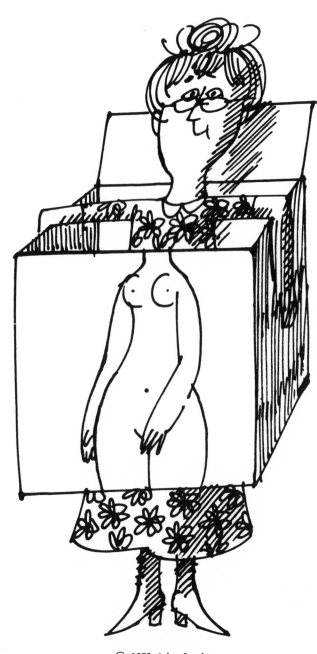

© 1972 Jules Stauber

"We've run out of virgins, O Mighty One! Will you accept a photographer from the 'National Geographic'?"

"That's right, Aunt Flo. Cousin Bernie, from Tenafly. My birthday's July 16th. I have a small mole on my left arm. You used to help me with math. _Now_ will you buzz the buzzer?"

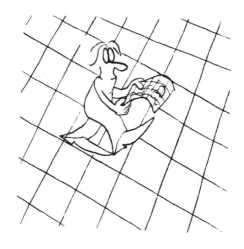

Stanislav Holý © Dikobraz

"I grant your point, but not because I agree with you. I'm under seda-tion."

"I danced the best I could, but what the guy really has is an iron deficiency."

"He's founding the English School of Watercolour or something."
© 1972 Michael ffolkes

Jean-Jacques Sempé © Denoël

"I think our commune is very, very fortunate to have you and your know-how, David."

KOREN

"We're planning a trip this summer to Area Codes 603, 802, and possibly 207."

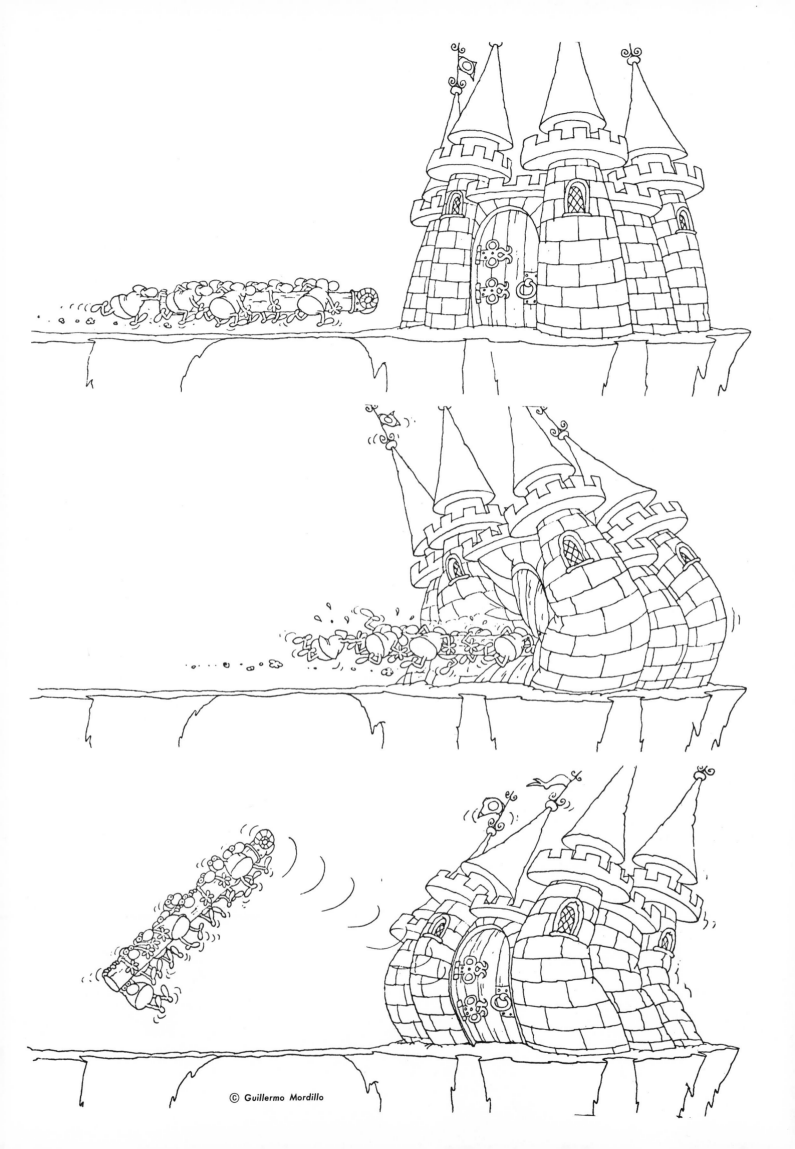

© Guillermo Mordillo

"Oh them—they play every Sunday—a foursome of supermarket
executives."
© 1972 Robert Day

Miroslav Barták © 1972 Dikobraz

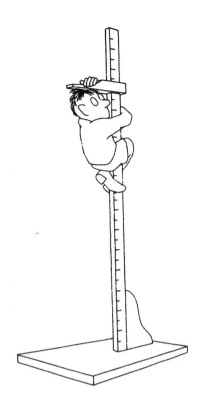

Miroslav Barták © 1972 Dikobraz

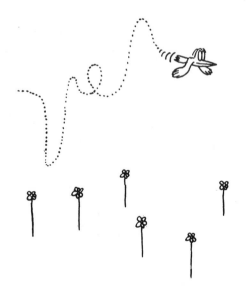

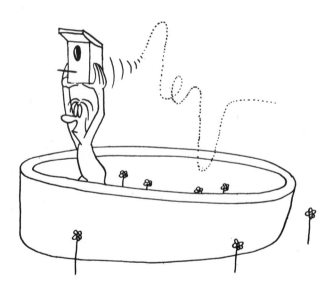

Stanislav Holý © Dikobraz

"I *am* the owner—an employee would have thrown you the hell out hours ago."
Boris Drucker © 1971 Look

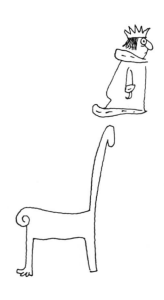

"That's right, **THE** Richard Burton! As far as I'm concerned **I** am **THE** Richard Burton!"
Leslie Starke © Punch

4

© 1972 Ton Smits

Terence Parkes © Punch

"Just between us, before those nature guys showed up and put bands
on everybody, I couldn't tell one damned penguin from another."

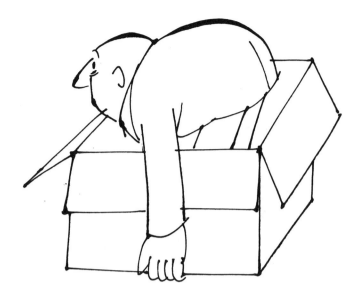

MORDILLO

© Guillermo Mordillo

"Are you going to believe me or some encyclopedia you picked up in a supermarket?"

1

ffolkes

"Do you find there are days when it's difficult to communic
© 1972 Michael ffolkes

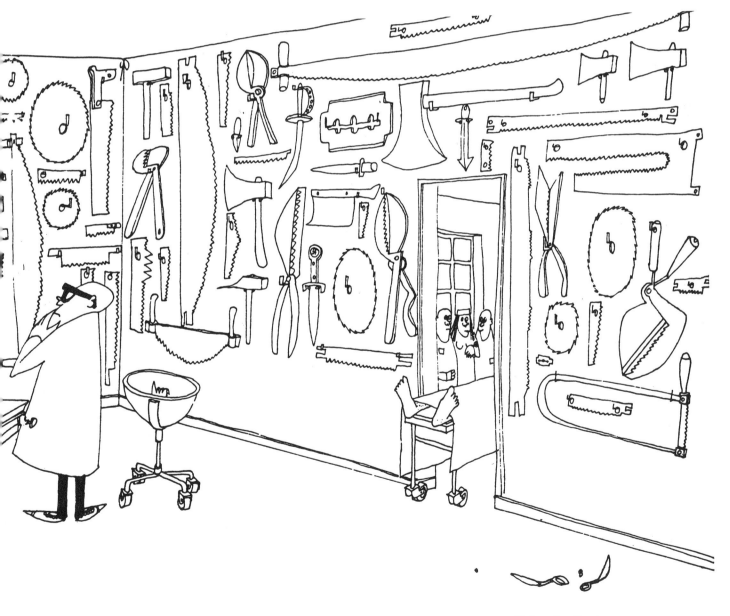

© Tony Munzlinger

"This is no longer a commune. It's a conglomerate!"
© 1972 Eldon Dedini

"Look out, Mrs. Barsley, it can smell fear."
© 1972 Michael ffolkes

"I rue the day I learned to delegate authority."

"I've been telling Doctor Szelik here about that chest of yours. He would like to have a look at it also."
Leslie Starke © Punch

"Charlie, why not try taking another of your sleeping pills?"
Alex Graham © Punch

"Gosh fellows, isn't there something you'd like to ask me?"

William O'Brian Copr. © 1972 The New Yorker Magazine, Inc.

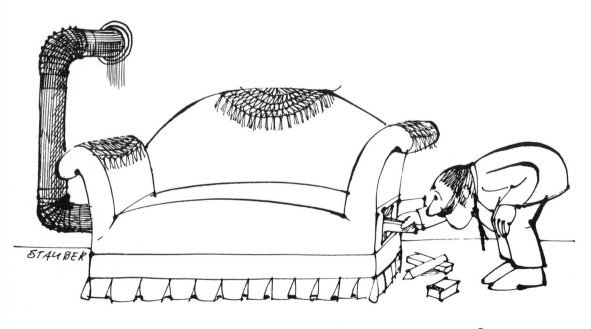

"What! Frozen fish fingers for lunch again?"
© Norman Thelwell

"The side door, Madame! Not the revolving door, Madame! The side door, Madame!"
© 1972 Robert Day

It is the 23rd of December.
This unemployed filing clerk has been
invited to attend the Christmas
OFFICE PARTY of the distillery where
he was formerly employed.

He visits his old office and is confronted by the head cooper.

Where's the OFFICE PARTY?

They're not having it here this year — it's in the HEad Office at Chancery Lane..

where it belongs

but seeing as you're here you may as well have a festive drink.

He is taken to an adjoining building.

Have ONE pint of gin, then get off to Chancery Lane — the men'll go mad if they find out there's an office worker here

He follows these instructions then sets out for Chancery Lane

He seeks directions from a member of the public

Malted Meths

Second hand clothing

Could you tell me how to get to Chancery Lane?

Dinner Suits our Specialty

92   92

DINNERS

Even were I sober enough to speak articulately, I wouldn't tell you.

He repeats this proceedure.

Chancery Lane?

First right
second left
right and right
again till
you come to
the roundabout then
left, left, right
left right left
right right left right ... .

He meticulously follows
these directions & arrives
at the zoo. The animals, sensing the approach of Xmas, are
unusually hostile.

Touch me just ONCE
with that chop and
I'll sue every zoo
in Africa

To sustain him in his quest, he enters an
hostelrie and is soon deep in conversation with
a playwright

I'm working on two
plays at once — the
first is about three
people shouting at each
other, the second is about
an old man sharpening
a knife....

$1\frac{1}{2}$ hours later:

I must get to Chancery Lane

Why don't you take a taxi?

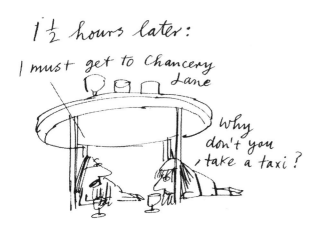

I've no money left

That's all right, all you have to do is direct the driver to the Law Courts and when the taxi stops at the traffic lights near Fleet Street, get out and run like a madman.

He pursues this course of action.

four letter words tightly constructed to convey the maximum of rage and bitterness

... with such zeal —

...hat when he arrives at
Chancery Lane he does
not notice an open
MANHOLE

and he falls

down

down

down

down

to

OBLIVION

"Come to bed."

"Speak, boy, speak!"
© 1972 Ton Smits

"But don't forget—that's with a bowling ball stuck on my thumb."
Reprinted with permission from THE SATURDAY EVENING POST © Chon Day

1

3

5

7

2

4

6

8

© Tony Munzlinger

© 1972 Anatol Kovarsky

Stanislav Holý © 1972 Dikobraz

"I'd like you to know that my husband and I are very, very impressed."
William O'Brian Copr. © 1971 The New Yorker Magazine, Inc.

"No chairs! They'll only stay longer!"
Jean-Jacques Sempé © Denoël

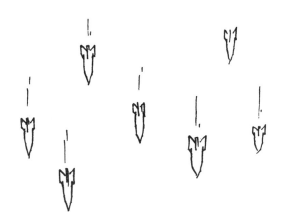

"This is terrible! I've just finished cleaning up."
Vladimir Renčin © Dikobraz

Stanislav Holý © Dikobraz

". . . and this is the present duke . . ."

Stanislav Holy © Dikobraz

"And this, gentlemen, is Mr. Quodley, my immediate inferior."

"I want you to realize that these people are unhappy. They are unhappy because they are desperate, and they are desperate because they are bored."

Jean-Jacques Sempé © Denoël

"Stop me, sire, if you're heard this one."

"Enjoy any great carrion lately?"
© 1972 Eldon Dedini

"More than anything I wish to be taken seriously."

Terence Parkes © Punch

"The computer is only a tool. There will always be a place for un-
bridled avarice."
Lee Lorenz Copr. © 1971 The New Yorker Magazine, Inc.

"I've just done a hole in one!"
Alex Graham © Punch

"D.F. of Tooting has signed the Rubens again."

Norman Thelwell © Punch

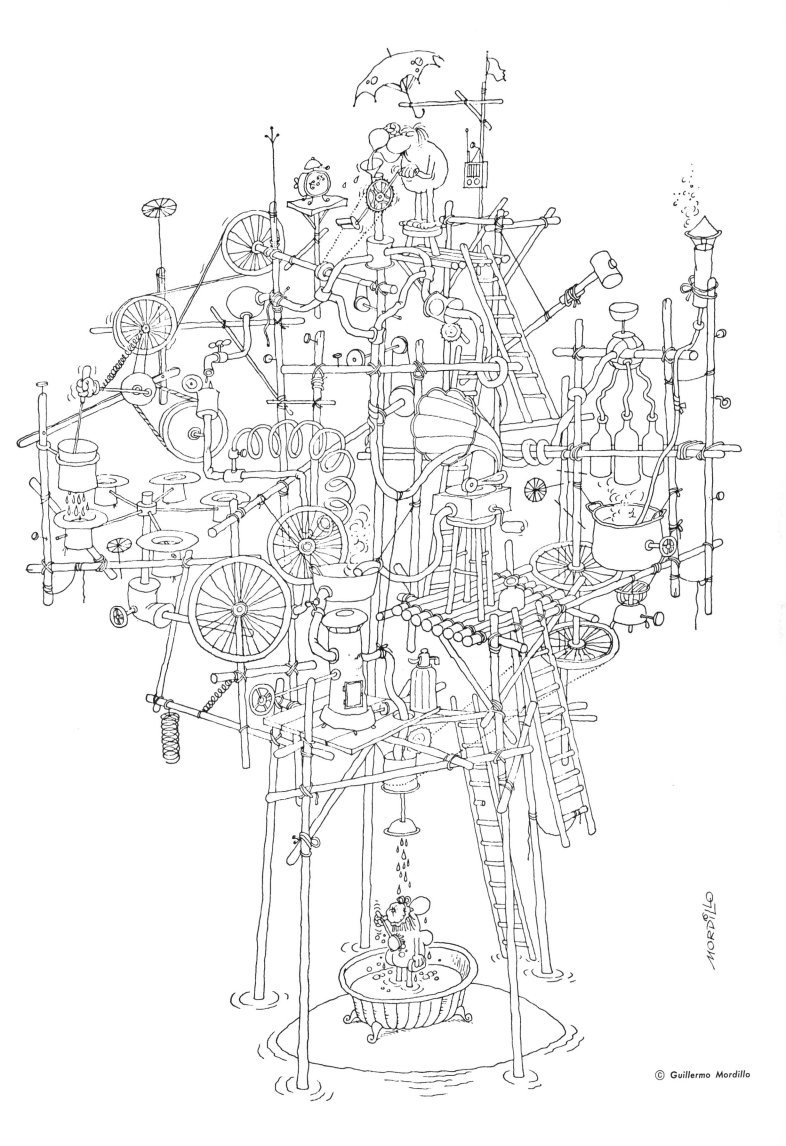

© Guillermo Mordillo

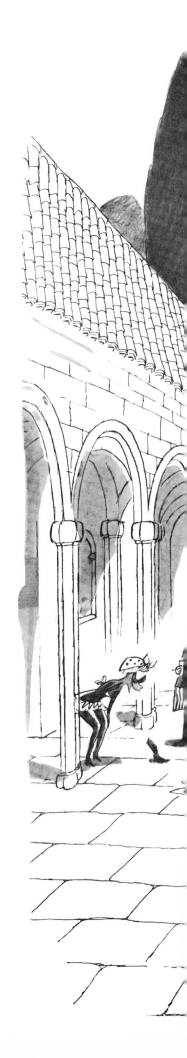

"The most difficult part of the alterations was to make sure we preserved the authentic character of the place."
Jean-Jacques Sempé © Denoël

"We're air-conditioned, but we're on the blink."

"I'm sorry, mate, it's a single-handed race."
© Norman Thelwell

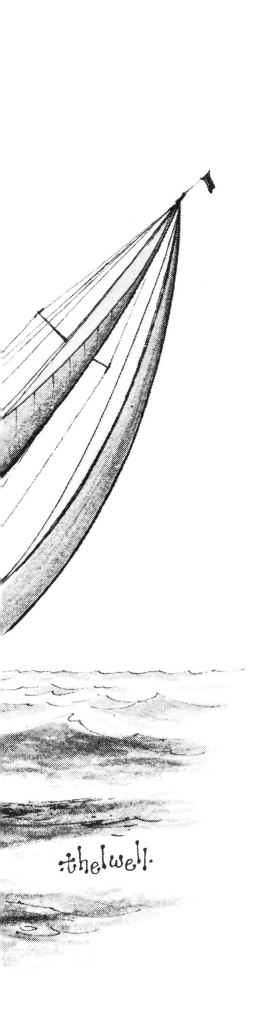

1

2

3

4   T.S.

"I know I speak for the group when I say that we're delighted to be here, and we look forward to working with you on projects of mutual interest in the days and years to come."

"Harry tried it last week. That's why he has no hair on his chest."
© 1972 Robert Day

"The artist flourished from 1720 to 1753. 'Flourished' is right!"

"We must wait for a wind. I do not wish to stand accused of unpro-
voked aggression."
Leslie Starke © Punch

"Why can't you collect shells like other kids?"

Terence Parkes © Punch

Terence Parkes © Punch

"Our minister said for us to become involved with community activities. Harry got his at a City Council tax protest demonstration, and I got mine at a School Board meeting."

© 1972 Robert Day

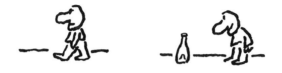

BOSC

© 1972 Bosc

"First, I want to thank the network for giving me this opportunity for rebuttal."

1

2

3

4

5

VAHAN SHIRVANIAN

Vahan Shirvanian © *1962 Look*

"Good morning, Mr. Postman. Good morning, ladies. Good morning,
Officer. Good morning, pussycat. Good morning, Your Eminence."

"First we will learn how one says, 'hello'—'whou, whou, whou, whaw'—
by tapping the mouth with the hand."
Jean-Jacques Sempé © Denoël

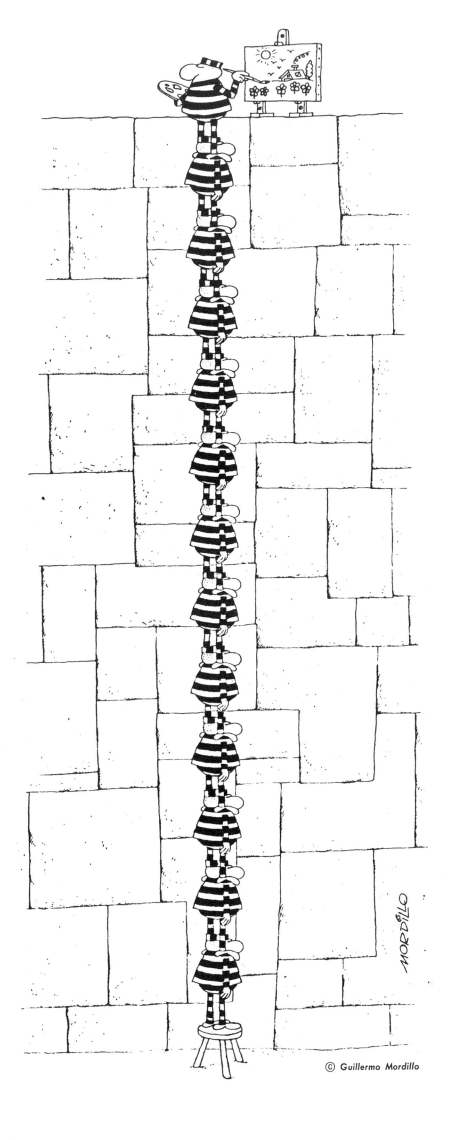

© Guillermo Mordillo

Alex Graham © Punch

"Beck and Call reporting."
Chon Day Copr. © 1969 The New Yorker Magazine, Inc.

"He's the vocalist."
© 1972 Hans Moser

© Guillermo Mordillo

"I had a dress once."

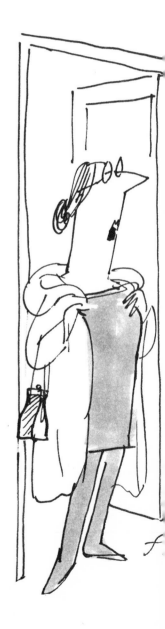

"No, Mr. Patterson, that's only if you're going to drown yourself."
© 1972 Michael ffolkes

1

2

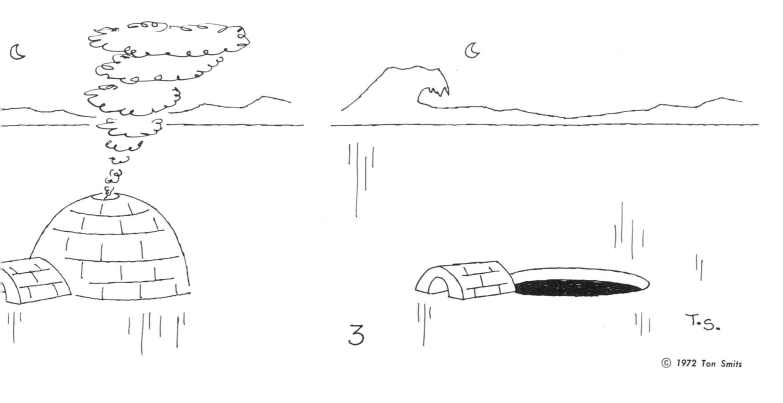

3

© 1972 Ton Smits

Vladimir Renčin © Czechoslovak Life

"All I said was that she looks like the kind of woman who would be easy on the budget."

Reprinted with permission from THE SATURDAY EVENING POST © Chon Day

"I hope I won't offend you, sir, if I say how much I admire the way you retain your Huck Finn charm."

sempé

"He's one thousand years old today!"